A little duck is in the
pond. 'Quack, quack,' said
the little duck.

Jelly and Bean see the
little duck in the pond.

'I am lost,' said the little duck. 'Will you help me look for my mum?'

'Yes. We will help you,'
said Jelly.
'Yes. We will help you,'
said Bean.

Jelly and Bean help the little duck look for his mum.

A big duck is on the grass.
'Quack, quack,' said the
big duck.

It is his mum. Mum jumps
in the pond. 'Quack,
quack.'

The little duck jumps on
his mum. The little duck is
happy.